I see 1 dog.

I see 2 birds.

I see 3 rabbits.

I see 4 frogs.

I see 5 mice.

I see fun!

6

Text copyright © 2004 by Scholastic Inc.
Illustrations copyright © 2004 by John Ueland.
All rights reserved. Published by Scholastic Inc.
Printed in the U.S.A.

ISBN 0-439-67660-6

5 6 7 8 9 10   23   12 11 10 09 08

SCHOLASTIC INC.
New York Toronto London Auckland Sydney
Mexico City New Delhi Hong Kong Buenos Aires